Spot the Odd One Out

by Genie Espinosa

ARCTURUS

ARCTURUS

This edition published in 2018 by Arcturus Publishing Limited
26/27 Bickels Yard, 151–153 Bermondsey Street,
London SE1 3HA

Author: Lisa Regan
Illustrator: Genie Espinosa
Editor: Susannah Bailey
Designer: Oakley Creative

ISBN: 978-1-78828-701-2
CH006293NT
Supplier 29, Date 0818, Print run 6985

Printed in China

ON THE ICE
Can you spot which animal doesn't belong here?

BALANCING ACT

Which of these cheerleaders is not wearing the correct uniform?

FISHY BUSINESS

Which fish doesn't match the rest of its family?

STOP, THIEF!

The pizza thief has stolen a sneaky slice. Which pizza has only five slices instead of six?

WE ARE SAILING

Which of the super cruisers has one fewer passenger?

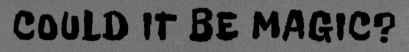

COULD IT BE MAGIC?

Can you spot a magical unicorn, playing in the meadow?

8

WEIGHT A MINUTE

Which of the weightlifter silhouettes is not an exact match for its strong owner?

SHOOTING STARS

Ooh! Ahh! Which of the fantastic shooting stars is a teeny bit different to the others?

HUNG OUT TO DRY

It is laundry day for the seven dwarfs. Whose spare socks are missing from this scene?

WELL, FANCY THAT!

Which of Madame Chapeau's fancy hats does not feature in the pages of her magazine?

PARTY BLOOPER

Which child did not read the invite correctly, and is not wearing a fun Halloween costume?

MALFUNCTION

One of the robots has come off the production line with a small fault. Can you see which one it is?

IN THE SWIM

Jimmy is ready to take the plunge! All of the outlines are a perfect match except one. Can you spot it?

DEAR DIARY

Katie keeps all of her secrets locked away. Her diary is the one that is a tiny bit different. Can you spot it?

HAPPY BIRTHDAY!

Find a single birthday cake for a five-year-old who likes trains.

DISTANT SHORES

Pirate Pete has a picture of his destination, but he arrives as night begins to fall. Which of the islands should he head to?

CHEEP!

Can you find a single yellow chick amongst the hens, ducks, and ducklings?

BUILD IT UP
Which container has not been used to build any of the sandcastles?

ROCK SCHOOL

Three guitar classes each have their own differently-shaped guitar. The teacher has her own special one. Which one is it?

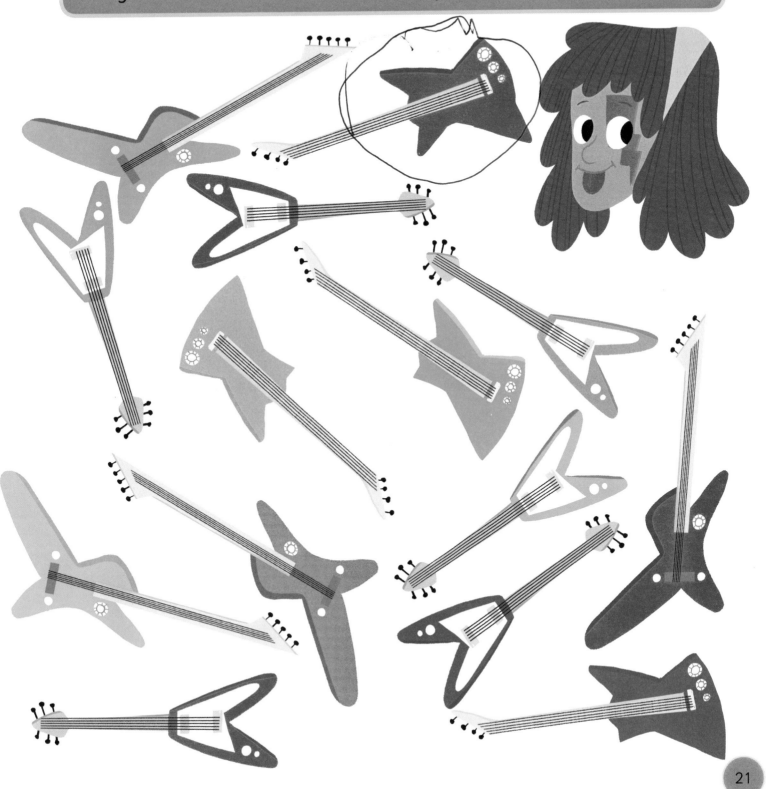

FAIRY TALE BALL

Here is the magical coach and horses to whisk you away! Which horse has not transformed in the same way as the others?

IN THE LAB

Oops! Which of the scientist silhouettes is not an exact match for the scientist herself?

STEP BACK IN TIME

Only one of the dinosaurs has two dino babies. Can you find the family with twins?

24

A DRAGON'S TALE

Which of the dragon scenes is not like any of the others?

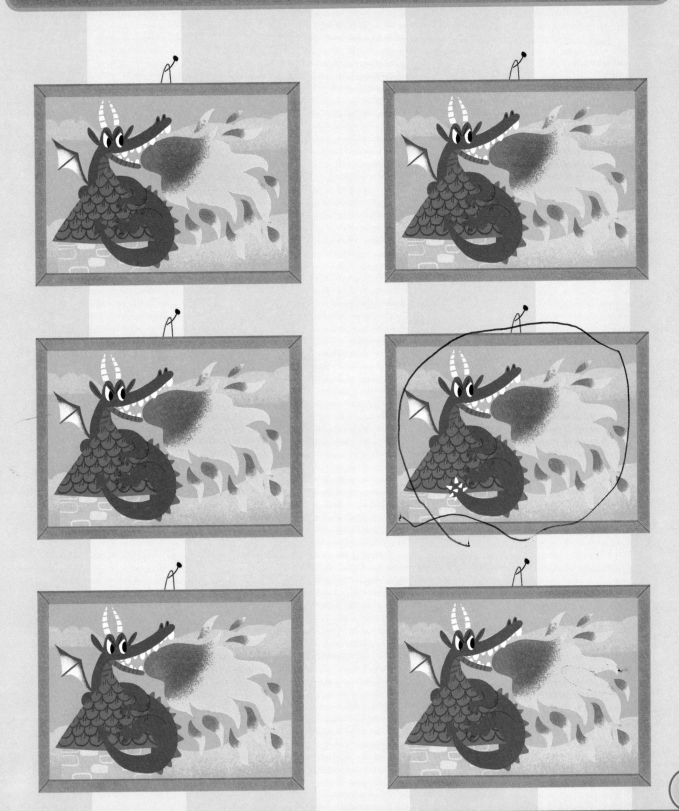

WONDER WEAVERS

Each type of spider makes a different style of web. Which spider has got it all wrong and woven a web with the wrong pattern?

GLORIOUS GATHERING

Which of these parrots is a tiny bit different from his friends?

COOKIE COTTAGE

Which of the gingerbread houses has been decorated differently?

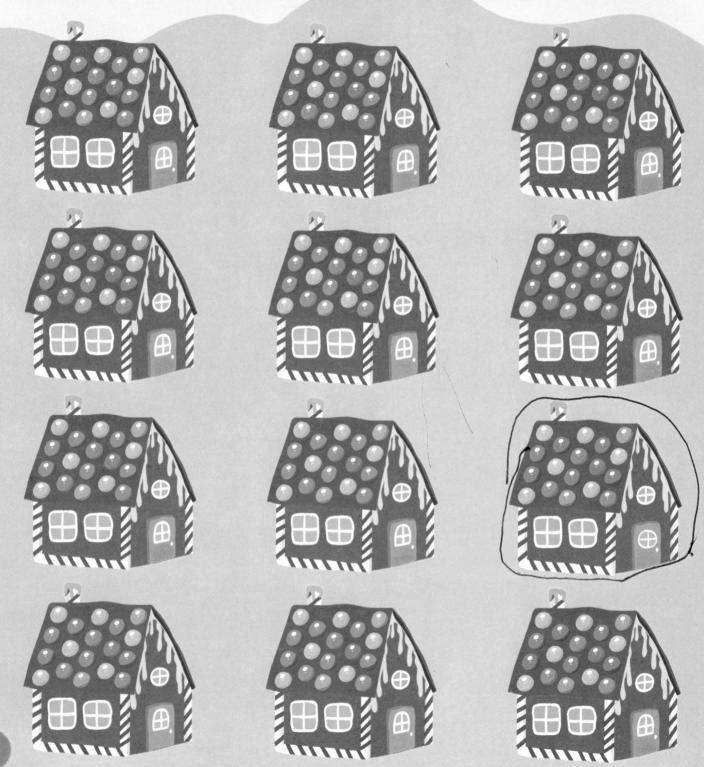

OUT OF TUNE

A member of the choir didn't read the dress code properly. Who has got it a little bit wrong?

LAUNDRY DAY

Pair up the socks to find one that is on its own.

Yes, of course he's riding a bike! How else would he get to school?
Which outline doesn't match the baboon in the middle?

FAST AND FLEET

Can you find a single yacht that only has yellow, orange, and white stripes on its sail?

JUNGLE JAPES

These tiny tapirs are just adorable, but one is different from the others. Can you spot it?

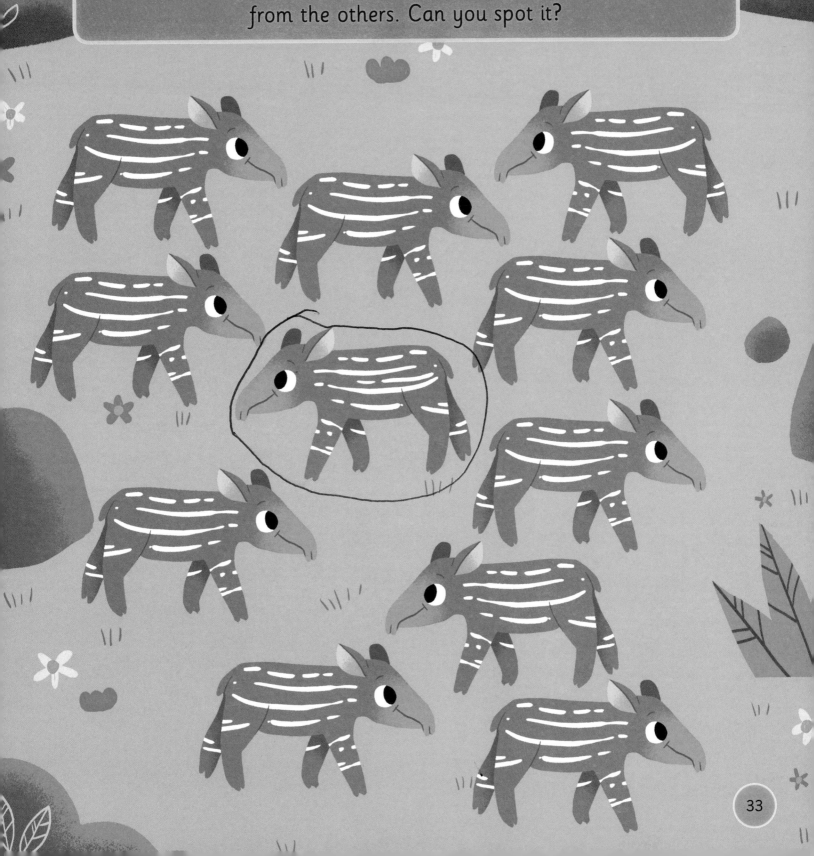

HOW DOES YOUR GARDEN GROW?

Mary's garden is full of beautiful flowers. Look carefully to find one of each that is a little bit different.

MODERN ART

Which of the forgeries has a mistake on it?

SHEEP SHUFFLE

Which of the herd has different markings from the rest?

SNOW TIME

Check out Louis on the ski slopes! Which of the outline shapes is not an exact match for the main picture?

Which of the dragons is a fearsome two-headed monster?

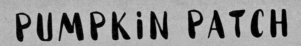

PUMPKIN PATCH

Can you spot the rogue carrot somewhere in the pumpkin patch?

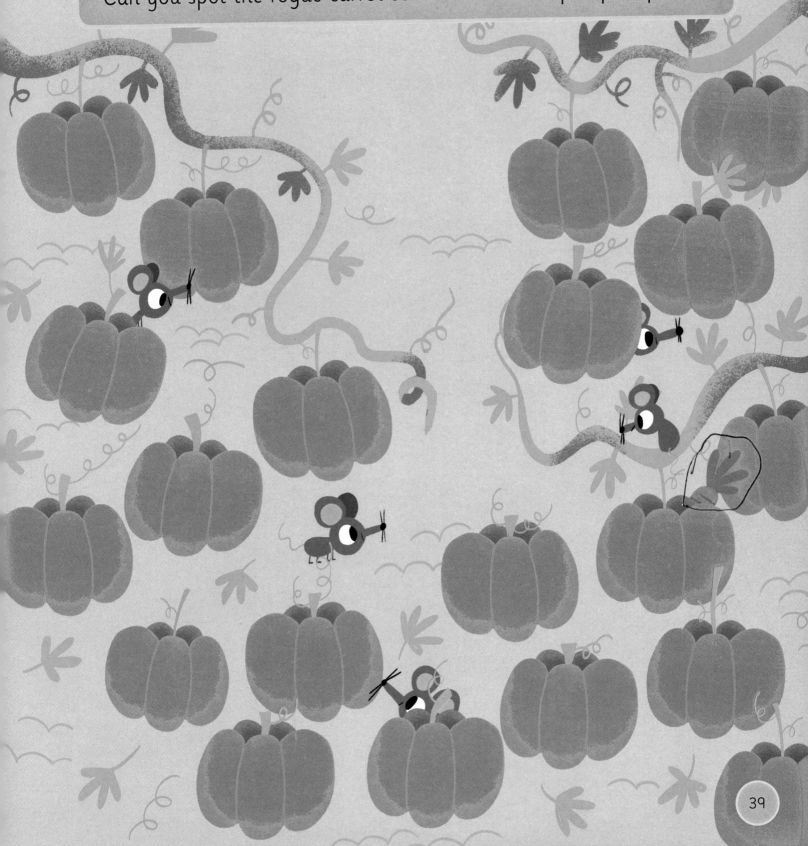

Which of the surfers' shorts do not match his or her board?

LAB TEST

Which bench does not contain all of the correct equipment to perform the class experiment?

CUCKOO'S NEST

The sneaky cuckoo lays an egg different to any other. In which nest has she laid it?'

FUNNY BONES

Can you spot the skeleton who looks different from his identical friends?

YUMMY... YUMMY... FUNNY

Which unique treat can you spot on the production line?

FLYING THE FLAG

Only one of these flags features an odd number of stars.
Can you find it?

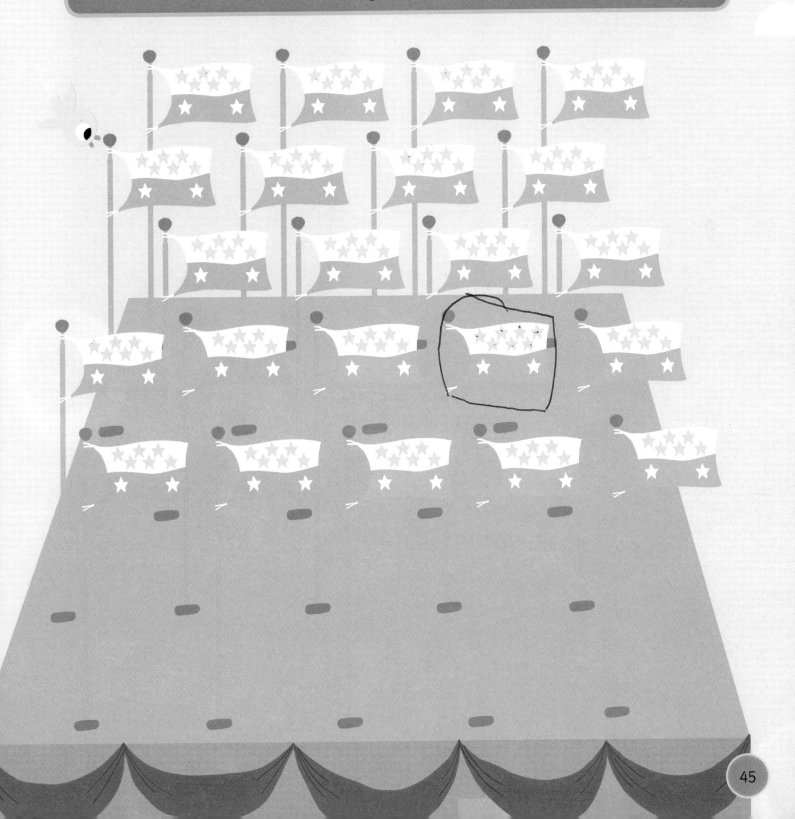

SPREAD YOUR WINGS

Which of the shadows does Fairy Sunshine leave behind when she flies away? It's the only one that matches her!

ABOUT TURN

Which of the kangaroos is facing the opposite way to the others?

EASY PISA

Which of the souvenirs has turned out slightly different from the rest?

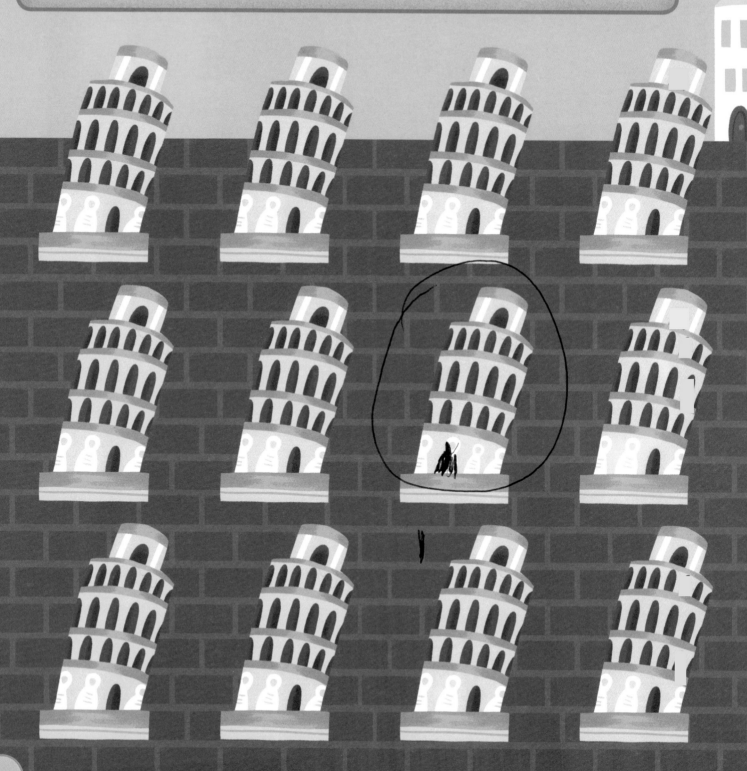

LEaf IT OUT!

One of the leaves in this pile is unlike all the others.
See if you can seek it out.

STARRY EYED

Only one of these stars has four points. Can you find it?

ON YOUR TRAIL

Can you find the single slug among the snails?

MONSTER MATCH

What's the size of a monster, but not quite as scary? A monster's shadow! Find the single shadow that isn't quite the same.

COLLECTION TIME

Which piece of luggage is missing its tag?

UNDER LOCK AND KEY

Each key opens a lock with matching decorations.
Which lock cannot be opened?

SPOTTED!

Which leopard has actually changed its spots?

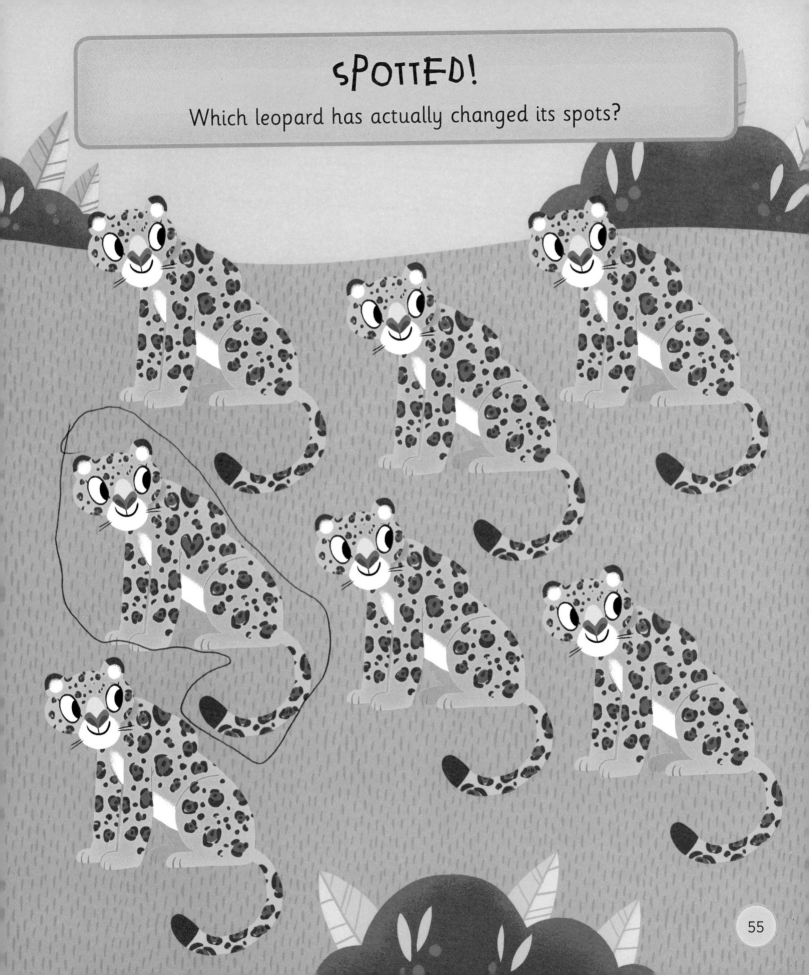

KEEP ON RUNNING

Which of the athletes is running solo, rather than with other club members in matching tops?

YEE-HA!

Which silhouette is the only one that doesn't match the rodeo rider exactly?

BLOOMING LOVELY

Which bouquet contains a single unique bloom?

ALL AT SEA

Which mermaid is the odd one out?

HELP TO HIDE

These mice are in disguise. Which one has forgotten something?

SKATE SHOP

Which of the skateboards is one of a kind?

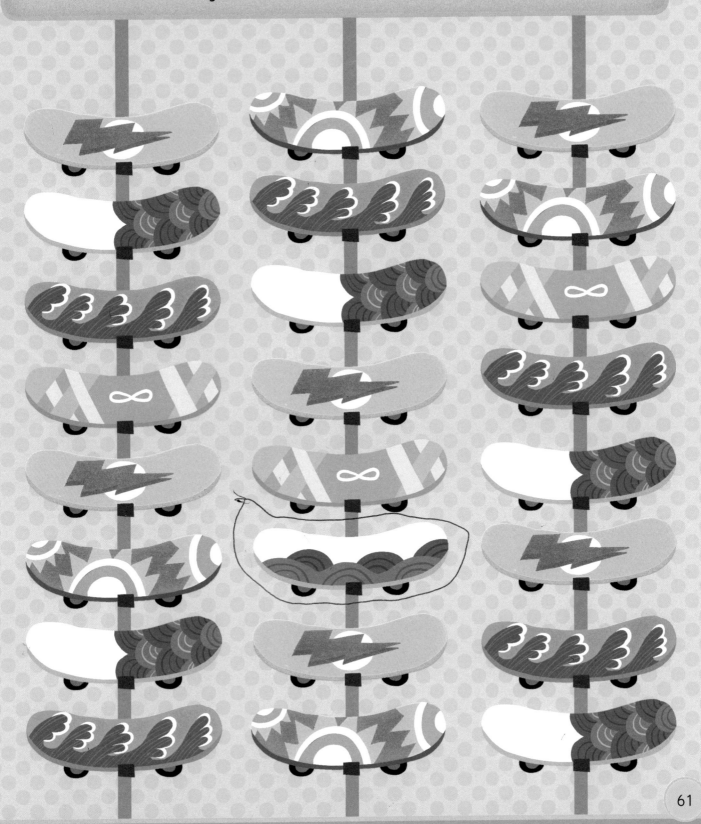

OUT OF STEP

Which dancer is a move behind the others?

PAWS FOR THOUGHT

Track down the single print that is not like any of the others.

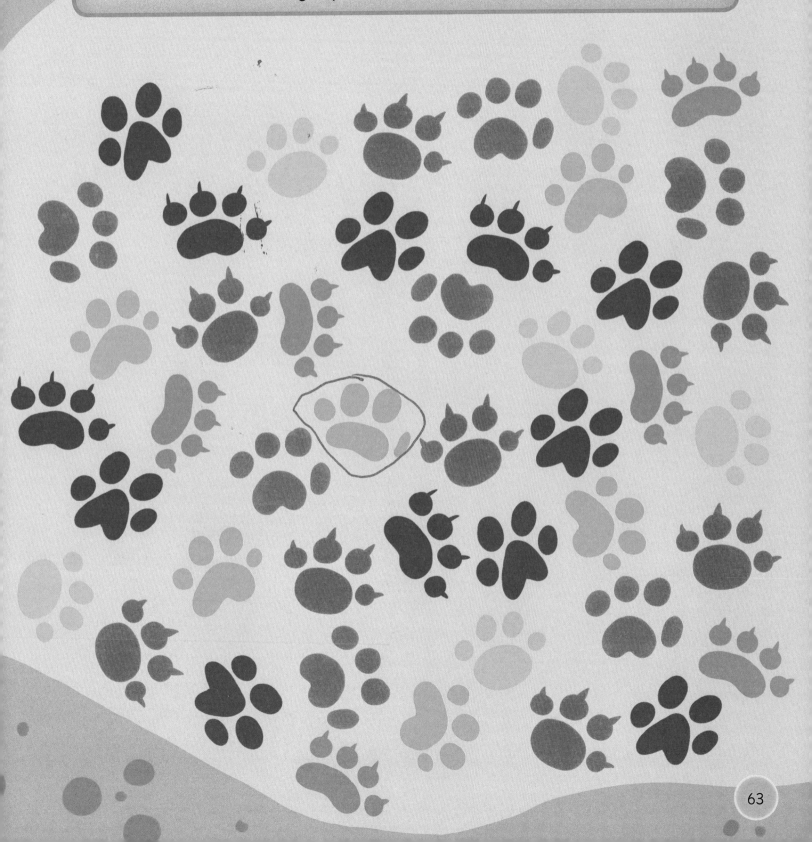

SCARECROW SCRAMBLE

Which of these scarecrow outlines is slightly different?

CLIFFHANGER

Which of these puffins has a body part that is a tiny bit different from the rest?

BALLOON SELLER

Pepe is looking for a balloon that looks funnier than the others.
Can you find one?

FEELING CRABBY

Which of the comical crabs is a tiny bit different from all the others?

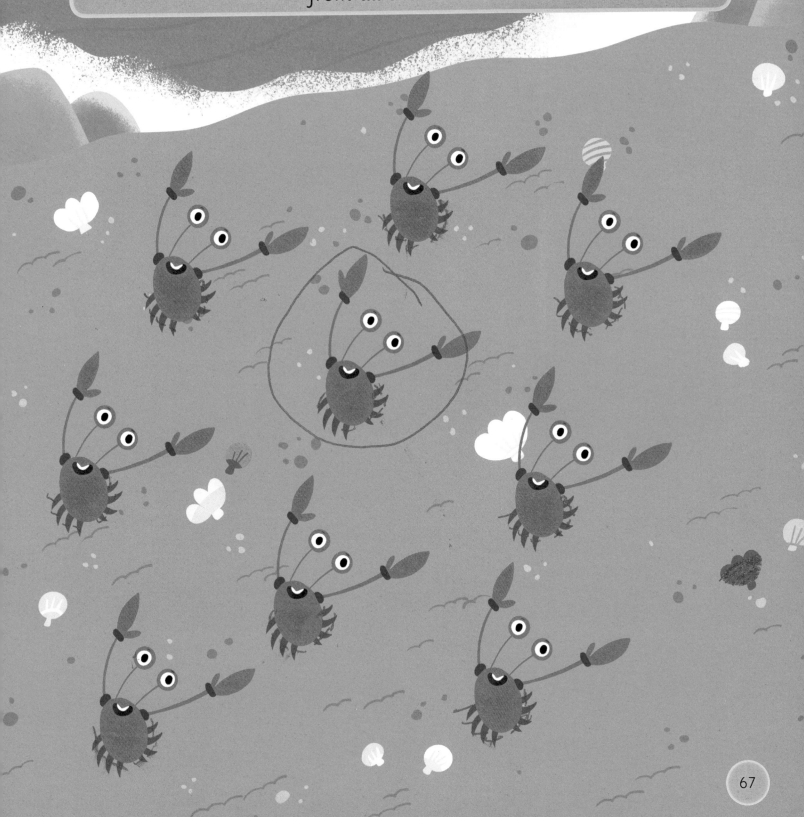

REaLLY ROYaL

Begging your pardon, your Highness, but one of these pictures is not quite the same. Which one is it?

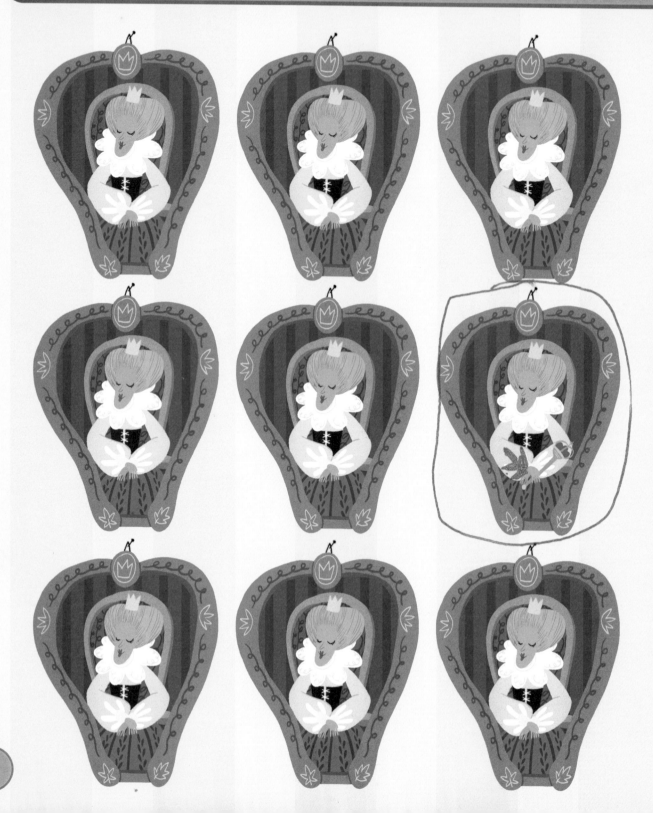

SUPER JUICE

Let's make smoothies! Which table has different ingredients from all the others?

ROLL UP! ROLL UP!

The circus is in town! Which of the shadow outlines is not an exact match for the performer?

DIVE IN

Which dolphin is swimming away from the group?

TRACTOR TROUBLE

See if you can help the farmer find his tractor. It is ever so slightly different from all the others on this page.

72

COOKING UP A STORM

Which of the chefs is armed with both a spoon
and a saucepan?

ALIEN INVASION

Only one of the UFOs is from the planet Blopp. It looks different from all the others. Can you find it?

74

HOME SWEET HOME

Fairy Daffodil is visiting her friend, Fairy Rose. She knows her home has six spots on the roof and two windows. Which door should she knock on?

MONSTER MASH

Look carefully to find a two-horned, three-eyed monster
at the monster ball.

FROGGY FUN

Find the silhouette that doesn't match the main picture.
Maybe he's the one that will turn back into a prince?

SUPERSONIC

Which of the stunt planes is the odd one out?

WATCH OUT!

Look closely to find a non-venomous king snake in the midst of the venomous coral snakes. Yikes!

NIGHT NIGHT

Which of the houses has all of its lights switched off,
ready for bed?

all at sea

One of the seahorse silhouettes does not match the main picture.
Can you "sea" which one it is?

I-SPY

Can you spot the one fruit that is different from the rest?

ON THE CATWALK

Which of the cats at the cowboy convention has forgotten to wear the right footwear?

SLOWLY DOES IT

Take your time to track down whose shell does not match any of the others.

FINDING THE WAY

See if you're heading in the right direction to find the odd one out in this selection.

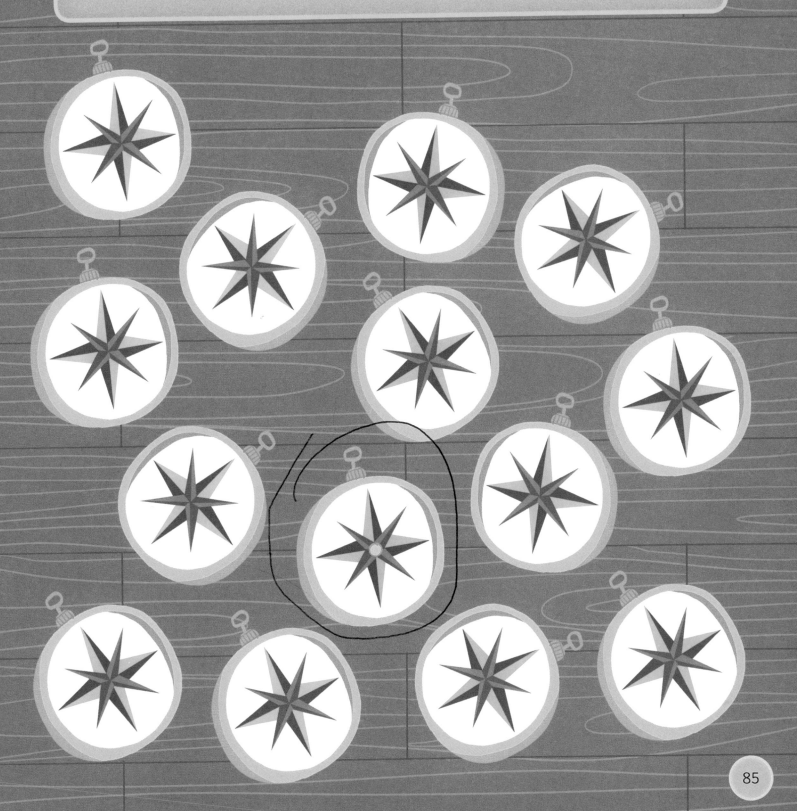

TAKE a HIKE

Which of these children is missing an item of uniform?

MIGHTY MONSTER

Which of these terrors of the high seas is looking more deadly than the rest?

ON TARGET

Use the scorecard to add up what each archer has scored.
Which target has a different score?

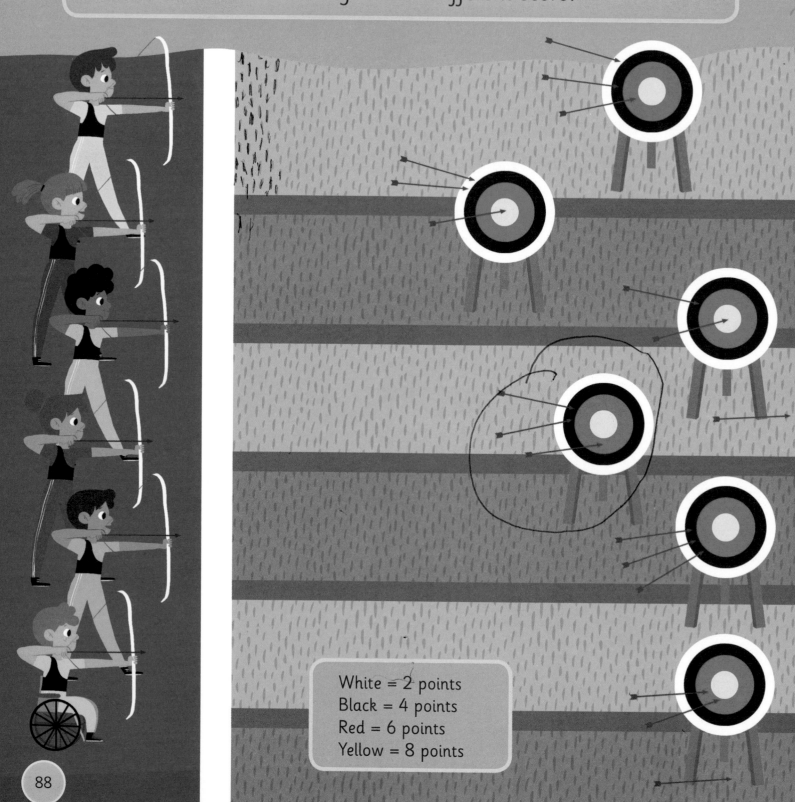

White = 2 points
Black = 4 points
Red = 6 points
Yellow = 8 points

ANSWERS

Page 3: On the Ice

Page 4: Balancing Act

Page 5: Fishy Business

Page 6: Stop, Thief!

Page 7: We are Sailing

Page 8: Could it be Magic?

Page 9: Weight a Minute

Page 10: Shooting Stars

Page 11: Hung Out to Dry

Page 12: Well, Fancy That!

Page 13: Party Blooper

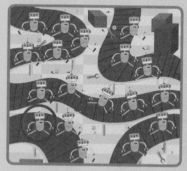

Page 14: Mal-function

Page 15: In the Swim

Page 16: Dear Diary

Page 17: Happy Birthday!

Page 18: Distant Shores

Page 19: Cheep!

Page 20: Build it Up

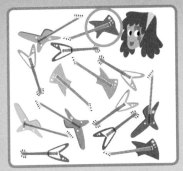

Page 21: Rock School

Page 22: Fairytale Ball

Page 23: In the Lab

Page 24: Step Back in Time

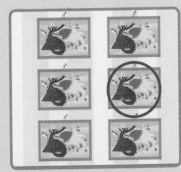

Page 25: A Dragon's Tale

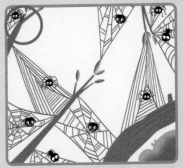

Page 26: Wonder Weavers

Page 27: Glorious Gathering

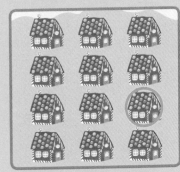

Page 28: Cookie Cottage

Page 29: Out of Tune

Page 30: Laundry Day

Page 31: Baboon on a Bike

Page 32: Fast and Fleet

Page 33: Jungle Japes

Page 34: How Does Your Garden Grow?

Page 35: Modern Art

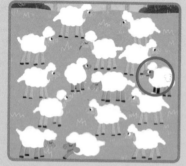

Page 36: Sheep Shuffle

Page 37: Snow Time

Page 38: Better Than One

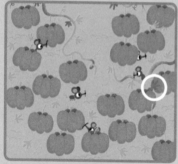

Page 39: Pumpkin Patch

Page 40: Super Surfers

Page 41: Lab Test

Page 42: Cuckoo's Nest

Page 43 Funny Bones

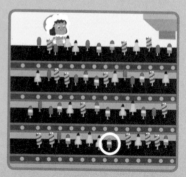

Page 44: Yummy...Yummy... Funny

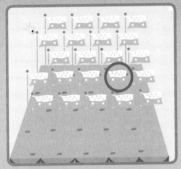

Page 45: Flying the Flag

Page 46: Spread Your Wings

Page 47: About Turn

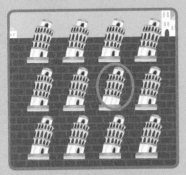

Page 48: Easy Pisa

Page 49: Leaf it Out!

Page 50: Starry Eyed

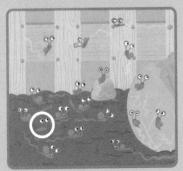

Page 51 On Your Trail

Page 52: Monster Match

Page 53: Collection Time

Page 54: Under Lock and Key

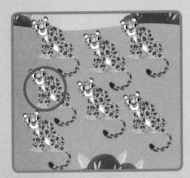

Page 55: Spotted!

Page 56: Keep on Running

Page 57: Yee-ha!

Page 58: Blooming Lovely

Page 59: All at Sea

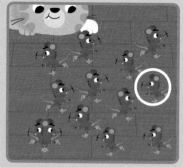

Page 60: Help to Hide

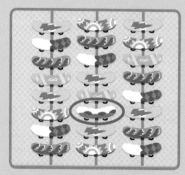

Page 61: Skate Shop

Page 62: Out of Step

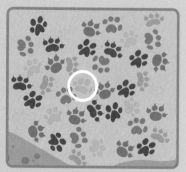

Page 63: Paws for Thought

Page 64: Scarecrow Scramble

Page 65: Cliffhanger

Page 66: Balloon Seller

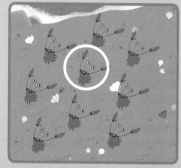

Page 67: Feeling Crabby

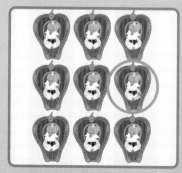

Page 68: Really Royal

Page 69: Super Juice

Page 70: Roll Up! Roll Up!

Page 71: Dive In

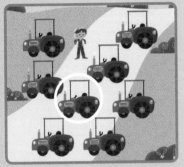

Page 72: Tractor Trouble

Page 73: Cooking Up a Storm

Page 74: Alien Invasion

Page75: Home Sweet Home

Page 76: Monster Mash

Page 77: Froggy Fun

Page 78: Supersonic

Page 79: Watch Out!

Page 80: Night Night

95

Page 81: All at Sea

Page 82: I-Spy

Page 80: On the Catwalk

Page 84: Slowly Does It

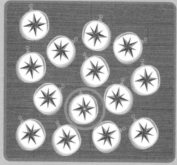

Page 85: Finding the Way

Page 86: Take a Hike

Page 87: Mighty Monster

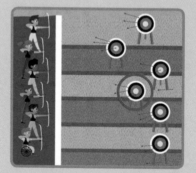

Page 88: On Target